To

_____

Love

_____

MW00948547

THE
PERFECT LULLABY

ISBN: 978-1-7346573-9-5 (Paperback)
ISBN: 978-1-7346573-8-8 (Hardcover)

Any references to historical events, real people, or real places are used fictitiously. Names, characters, and places are products of the author's imagination.

Written by Brittany Plumeri
Illustrated and designed by Charanya Kalamegam
Edited by Vicky Weber

First printing edition 2021

www.onceuponapagepress.com

To my babies, Noah and Ella-
Thank you for showing me that there is no limit to the amount of love one can feel.

It's bedtime my child so snuggle me close
It's time for a song that you'll treasure the most

I think of my favorites from when I was young
Each one is unique but which one should be sung?

Perhaps I should sing you the one with the star.
...Would that make you wonder who you really are?

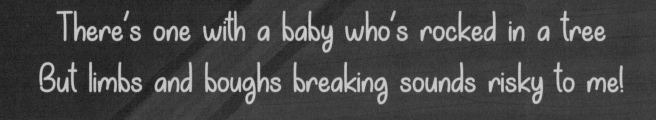

There's one with a baby who's rocked in a tree
But limbs and boughs breaking sounds risky to me!

I would sing a song of a prized mockingbird
But a bird and a goat as a gift seems absurd

I might sing the rhyme with the cow and the moon
But does that dish flee with a fork or a spoon?

I'm thinking of songs...but you don't make a peep.
And that's when I notice you've drifted to sleep

While lost in my musings. How could I not see?
Your favorite lullaby's coming from me.

The music of love rings so clear and so true.
It comes from my heart... which is beating for you.

About the Author

Brittany is a bestselling author, a mom, and an elementary school teacher. Her inspiration from her stories comes from the children she loves, both in her home and in her classroom.

The Perfect Lullaby was inspired one night while she was rocking her son, Noah to sleep. She sat there for what seemed like forever trying to figure out the perfect song, to sing, but before she was able to pick one, she looked down and saw that he was already fast asleep on her chest to the only true lullaby a new baby really needs — mom's heartbeat.

About the Illustrator

Charan, (Charanya Kalamegam) is a freelance illustrator, who's love for art has been ever-growing since childhood. She puts her passion into illustrating children's books, exhibiting her art, preparing art prints, and most of all enjoy life.

After graduating from Newcastle University, England, she took a break from Architecture, only to find a new journey to enjoy and cherish her true passion.

Her art is always inspired by nature and life, and brings out the best relationship between them. Some of her works include Hany and Nuts series, Walk with Sammy, Ada's adventure and more in working.

Find her works online by the name HUEbyCharan.

Other books by Brittany

Teaching kindness
has never been so

fun!

Don't forget to leave a review!

★★★★★

CPSIA information can be obtained
at www.ICGtesting.com
Printed in the USA
LVHW070309230723
752993LV00007B/302